David —

May you be the
magnet for all good
people & opportunities you
deserve!

—PB

MAGNETIC
CURRENT

MAGNETIC
CURRENT

BY
EDWARD LEEDSKALNIN

Cover, "Pixii's Magneto-Electric Machine," credit Wellcome Collection

Cover Design by Matthew Johnson, © 2022 Mockingbird Press, LLC

Foreword by Mary Beck, Copyright © 2022 Mockingbird Press, LLC

Publisher's Cataloging-In-Publication Data

Leedskalnin, Edward, author; with Beck, Mary, foreword by Magnetic Current / Edward Leedskalnin; with Mary Beck

Paperback   ISBN-13: 978-1-68493-056-2
Hardback   ISBN-13: 978-1-68493-057-9
Ebook   ISBN-13: 978-1-68493-058-6

1. Science—Physics—Magnetism. 2. Mathematics—Physics—Electricity, Electromagnetism & Magnetism, I. Edward Leedskalnin. II. Mary Beck. III. Magnetic Current

SCI038000 / PHK

Type Set in Century Schoolbook / **Franklin Gothic Demi**

Mockingbird Press, Augusta, GA
info@mockingbirdpress.com

FOREWORD

MAGNETIC Current is a short pamphlet by eccentric sculptor and writer Edward Leedskalnin. Detailing his many experiments with magnets, this work posits that it is not metal itself that is magnetic. Rather, tiny individual magnet particles that circulate in and around the metal give it its pull.

Edward Leedskalnin was born in Latvia in 1887. While his formal education lasted only until 4th grade, he was intensely curious and spent much of his youth reading. At the age of 26, Leedskalnin was engaged to marry a young woman named Agnes Skuvst. But as she was only 16, she (or her mother) decided that he wasn't a suitable match and called off the wedding the day before it was set to occur.

Heartbroken, Leedskalnin emigrated to the United States. He spent several years in the Pacific Northwest, where he contracted tuberculosis. After his recovery, he moved to Florida where he hoped the mild climate would be better for his health. In 1923, he purchased an undeveloped acre of land in Florida City, where he began an ambitious project that would absorb the next 28 years.

It was called Rock Gate, and it would eventually consist of over 1,100 tons of hand-carved oolite stone. Leedskalnin cut massive pieces of the rock from his property, moved them, and sculpted them—all on his own. Rock Gate was both project and home. He built a two-story tower from oolite, which served as his living quarters. In the grounds below, sculptures and carved stone furniture dot the landscape. The project was dedicated to his "Sweet Sixteen," the woman who rejected him years before.

Sometimes referred to as "Florida's Stonehenge" because of the size and scale of the undertaking, no one is entirely certain how the megalith project was completed. But it's especially impressive considering Leedskalnin was only 5 feet tall and weighed barely 100 pounds.

During the years of his construction project, Leedskalnin also conducted experiments and wrote several pamphlets. For two of those years, he studied and tested magnets from his home base of Rock Gate. His findings were eventually compiled into *Magnetic Current*, a short pamphlet detailing his theories of magnetism.

The pamphlet explains many of his experiments which can be replicated if one wishes. Using U-shaped, round, and bar magnets, as well as car batteries, light bulbs, and coils of wire, he demonstrates the movements of magnetic currents in a double helix pattern, swirling around each other to create pull.

Within the structure of the north/south pole magnet, Leedskalnin found answers to not only simple magnetism, but to greater questions of the universe. "The earth itself is a great big magnet," he states. Individual magnets—not the metal that we think of as a magnet, but the microscopic magnets that circulate the metal—emerge from each pole and run to the other, creating permanent magnetism.

"North and South Pole magnets are not only holding together the earth and moon, but they are turning the earth around on its axis," he writes. In his view, a reversal in the polarity of either the earth or the moon would lead to the moon crashing down to earth.

With his lack of formal education and English as a second language, the meaning of Leedskalnin's writings can be a challenge to decipher. But for students of magnetism, electricity, or currents, this work makes an interesting study. Perhaps it is his lack of formal education that led him to look at the mysteries of magnetism in a unique way.

Edward Leedskalnin died in 1951 of kidney failure—possibly due in part to his diet of crackers and sardines. His life's work can still be explored, both through his writings and by visiting Rock Gate (now called Coral Castle) which is a tourist attraction in Homestead, Florida.

MAGNETIC CURRENT

THIS writing is lined up so when you read it you look East, and all the description you will read about magnetic current, it will be just as good for your electricity.

Following is the result of my two years' experiment with magnets at Rock Gate, seventeen miles Southwest from Miami, Florida. Between Twenty-fifth and Twenty-sixth Latitude and Eightieth and Eighty-first Longitude West.

First, I will describe what a magnet is. You have seen straight bar magnets, U shape magnets, sphere or ball magnets and Alnico magnets in many shapes, and usually a hole in the middle. In all magnets one end of the metal is North Pole and the other South Pole, and those which have no end one side is North Pole and the other South Pole.

Now about the sphere magnet. If you have a strong magnet, you can change the poles in the sphere in any side you want or take the poles out so the sphere will not be a magnet any more. From this you can see that the magnet can be shifted and concentrated and also you can see that the metal is not the real magnet. The real magnet is the substance that is circulating in the metal. Each particle in the substance is an individual magnet by itself, and both North and South Pole individual magnets. They are so small that they can pass through everything. In fact, they can pass through metal easier than through the air. They are in constant motion, they are running one kind of magnets against the other kind, and if guided in the right channels they possess perpetual power. The North and South Pole magnets they are cosmic force, they hold together this earth and everything on it. Each North and South Pole magnet is equal in strength, but the strength of each individual magnet doesn't amount to anything. To be of practical use they will have to be in great numbers.

In permanent magnets they are circulating in the metal in great numbers, and they circulate in the following way. Each kind of the magnets are coming out of their own end of the pole and are running around, and are running in the other end of the pole and back to its own end, and then over and over again. All the individual magnets do not run around. Some run away and never come back, but new ones take their place.

The earth itself is a great big magnet. In general, these North and South Pole individual magnets are circulating in the same way as in the permanent magnet metal. The North Pole individual magnets are coming out of the earth's South Pole and are running around in the earth's North Pole and back to its own pole, and South Pole individual magnets are coming out of the earth's North Pole and are running around, and in earth South Pole and back to its own end. Then both North and South Pole individual magnets start to run over and over again.

In a permanent magnet bar between the poles there is a semi-neutral part where there is not much going in or out, but on the earth there is no place where the magnets are not going in or out, but the magnets are running in and out at pole ends more than at the Equator. Now you get the equipment and I will tell you so you can see for yourself that it is in the way I have told. Get a permanent magnet bar four inches long. A U shape magnet that is strong enough to lift from ten to twenty pounds. An Alnico magnet about three inches long, two and one-half inches wide, one inch thick. Hole in the middle and poles in each end, several feet in length of hard steel fishing line. Line when it is not in coil it stays straight and a soft steel welding rod one-eighth of an inch thick and three feet long. From the fishing wire and the welding rod you will make magnets or compasses, and if you hang them up in fine threads by middle and keep them there, they will be permanent magnets.

When you are making a magnet pole in the welding rod use U shape magnet. South Pole magnet to make North Pole magnet in the rod and use U shape North Pole magnet to make South Pole magnet in the rod. You can drag the magnet over the rod from end to end, but never stop in middle. If you stop in middle there will be an extra pole so it will disturb the magnet's circulation. Use iron filings to test the rod if there is any magnets in the middle, and if there is the filings will cling to it. Then drag the permanent magnet over the rod and it will take it out. To take the magnet out from rod ends approach or touch the rod end with the same kind of magnet that is in the rod, by dipping the rod ends in iron filings, you will see how it works.

Break three pieces of the steel fishing line just long enough to go in between the two poles of U shape permanent magnet. Put them endwise between the two poles, and take them out. Hang one by middle with fine thread, and hang it up in East side of the room where there is no other magnet or metal around. Now you will have a permanent magnet or compass to test the polarity in other magnets. For more delicate use hang the magnet in spider web. To test the strength of a magnet use iron filings.

Put the U shape permanent magnet two feet West from the hanging magnet. Hold the North Pole magnet in level with the hanging magnet, then you will see that the South pole of the hanging magnet is turning to you and the North Pole magnet away from you. Now put the South Pole permanent magnet pole in the same level, this time North Pole magnet will turn to you and South Pole magnet away from you. This experiment shows two things, one that the magnets can be sent out in straight streams, and the other whatever kind of magnets you are sending out the other kind of magnets are coming back to you.

Take two pieces of steel fishing line wire, put them in U shape magnet, hold a little while, take them out, bend a little back in one end and hang them up, and make it so that one magnet's lower end is North Pole magnet and the other South Pole magnet. Make it so that they hang three inches apart. Put North Pole North side, and South Pole South side. Now take the four-inch-long permanent magnet bar, hold North Pole in North side and South Pole in South side. Raise slowly up to the two hanging magnets, then you will see that the hanging magnets are closing up. Now reverse, put North Pole of bar magnet South side and South Pole North side. This time when bar magnet approaches the hanging magnets will spread out. This experiment shows that North and South Pole magnets are equal in strength and that the streams of individual magnets are running one kind of magnets against the other kind.

Cut a strip of a tin can about two inches wide and a foot long. Put the North Pole of the U shape magnet on top of the strip, and dip the lower end in iron filings, and see how much it lifts. Now put the South Pole on top and see how much it lifts. Change several times, then you will see that the North Pole lifts more than the South Pole. Now put the North Pole magnet under the iron filing box, and see how much it pushes up. Now change, put South Pole magnet under the box and see how much it pushes up. Do this several times, then you will see that the South Pole magnet pushes up more than North Pole magnet. This experiment shows again that on level ground the magnets are in equal strength.

Now take the three-foot long soft steel welding rod. It is already magnetized as a permanent magnet, hang it in a fine thread so it is in level. Now measure each and you will see that the South end is longer. In my location at Rock Gate, between Twenty-fifth and Twenty-sixth Latitude and Eightieth and Eighty-first Longitude West, in three-foot long magnet the South Pole end is about a sixteenth of an inch longer. Farther North it should be longer yet, but at Equator both ends of the magnet should be equal in length. In earth's South hemisphere the North Pole end of magnet should be longer.

All my hanging magnets or compasses they never point to the earth's magnetic pole, neither to the geographical pole. They point a little Northeast. The only reason I can figure out why they point in that way is, looking from the same geographical meridian the North magnetic pole is on, the South magnetic pole is one hundred and fifteen longitudes West from it. In rough estimation the earth's South magnetic pole is two hundred and sixty miles West from the same meridian the earth's North magnetic pole is on. That causes the North and South Pole magnets to run in Northeast and Southwest direction. My location is too far away from the magnetic poles so all my magnets are guided by the general stream of individual North and South Pole magnets that are passing by.

Now I will tell you what magnetic current is. Magnetic current is the same as electric current is a wrong expression. Really it is not one current, they are two currents, one current is composed of North Pole individual magnets in concentrated streams and the other is composed of South Pole individual magnets in concentrated streams, and they are running one stream against the other stream in whirling, screwlike fashion, and with high speed. One current alone if it be North Pole magnet current or South Pole magnet current it cannot run alone. To run one current will have to run against the other.

Now I will tell you how the currents are running when they come out of a car battery, and what they can do. Now get the equipment. First put a wooden box on floor, open side up, cut two notches in middle so you can put a one-eighth of an inch thick and eighteen-inch-long copper wire across the box. Put the wire one end East, the other West. Stay yourself West, put car battery South side of the box positive terminal East, negative terminal West, get two flexible leads and four clips to fit the battery and the bare copper wire, connect the East end of the copper wire with positive terminal, clip the West end of the copper wire with the West side flexible lead, leave the connection with negative terminal open.

Break two pieces of the steel fishing line one inch long, put each piece by middle across the copper wire, one on top of the copper wire and the other under, hold with your fingers, now touch the negative terminal with the loose clip, hold until the copper wire gets hot. Take them off, now you have two magnets, hang them up by middle in fine thread. The upper magnet will hang the way it is now, but the one below will turn around. Break five inches long piece of the fishing line, put the middle of the wire across and on top of the copper wire, touch the battery, hold until the copper wire gets hot, dip the middle of the wire in iron filings, then you will see how long a magnet can be made with this equipment.

Break or cut several pieces of the hard steel fishing wire as long as to go between the poles of the U shape magnet, now hold two pieces of the steel wire ends up and down, one wire South side of the copper wire, and the other North side, the lower ends just below the copper wire. Hold tight and touch the battery, hold until the copper wire gets hot, now hang them up by upper end just above the copper wire, touch battery, the South side magnet will swing South, and the North side magnet will swing North. Put two pieces on top of the copper wire, the ends just a little over the copper wire. Those ends lying on copper wire, one pointing South and the other North, hold tight, touch battery, hold until the copper wire gets hot, take off the one pointing South is South Pole magnet and the one pointing North is North pole magnet. Put one wire on top of the copper wire pointing South, other below pointing North. Magnetize, hang up by tail ends on the copper wire, touch battery; they both will swing South. Put one wire on top of the copper wire pointing North, the other below pointing South, magnetize, hang up by tail end above the copper wire, touch the battery, both magnets will swing North.

Cut six pieces of fishing wire one inch long, put them by middle on top and across the copper wire. Hold tight, touch battery, hold until copper wire gets hot. Take off, now put glass over the copper wire, put those six pieces of magnets on glass, on top of the copper wire lengthwise just so the ends don't touch each other, touch the battery, they all will turn across the copper wire, now pull three to South side and three to North side in the same way, they lie now but about one-half of an inch away from the copper wire, touch battery, they all will jump on the copper wire. Now roll all six together, let loose, and you will see that they won't stay together. Magnetize one piece in U shape magnet, put North Pole end East on the copper wire, and South Pole West, touch the battery, the magnet will swing left. Now put South Pole East side and North Pole West side, this time the magnet will turn right, take glass off.

Take one piece of hard steel fishing wire, dip in iron filings and see there is no magnet in it. This time hold the wire up and down, the lower end on middle of the copper wire, hold tight. Touch the battery, hold until the copper wire gets hot. Take it off. Dip the wire in iron filings and you will see that it is no magnet. Why? To make magnets with currents from batteries and dynamos with a single wire the metal will have to be put on the wire in such a way so that the magnets which are coming out of the wire will be running in the metal starting from the middle of the metal and run to the end and not from end to middle and across as they did this last time. You have read that to make a South Pole in a coil end that is pointing to you, you will have to run positive electricity in the coil in clockwise direction. I can tell you that the positive electricity has nothing to do with making a South magnet pole in the coil. Each pole South or North is made by their own magnets in the way they are running in the wire. This magnet-making with a single wire, it illustrates how all magnets are made.

In a car battery the North Pole magnets run out of positive terminal and South Pole magnets run out of negative terminal. Both kinds of magnets are running, one kind of magnets against the other kind, and are running in the same right-hand screw fashion. By using the same whirling motion and running one kind of magnets against the other kind, they throw their own magnets from the wire in opposite directions. That is why if you put a magnet metal across the copper wire the one end is North Pole and the other end South Pole.

Get four pieces of wire size sixteen, six inches long, two copper and two soft iron, bend one end of each wire back so the clips can hold it better. Use copper wire first. Put both wires in clips, connect with battery, have the wire ends square, now put the loose ends together, and pull them away. Then you will notice that something is holding you back. What is it? They are magnets. When you put the ends together, the North and South Pole magnets are passing from one wire to the other, and in doing it they pull the wire ends together. Now put the soft iron wire in the clips, put the loose ends together, and pull them away. This time the passing magnets hold the wire ends together stronger. Put the ends together many times, then you will see which wire end gets red first, and which will make the bigger bubble in the end, and watch the little sparks coming out from the bubbles. Stretch the bubbles out while they are in liquid form, then you will see in the bubble that something is whirling around. Those little sparks you see coming out of the bubble, they are not the magnets, but the magnets are the ones which throw the sparks out of the bubbles. When all the magnets that are in the wire, if they cannot pass over to the other wire, they are expending the bubble and running out of it and carrying the metal sparks with them. When the bubble is cool, break it up, then you will see the space left where the magnets were in.

Get two pieces of lumber, one by six inches, a foot long, nail them together so that one lies flat on floor and the other on top, the edges up and down. Cut a notch in end in upper piece, four inches deep and as high as to hold a piece of wood or brass that would hold needle points in ends and have a hole in middle to hold the three-foot magnet. Balance the magnet good so it would stop on its right magnetic position. Now put the car battery South side positive terminal East and negative terminal West. Connect the East end of the copper wire with positive terminal and connect the West end of the copper wire with the West side lead, hold the copper wire just above the magnet a quarter of an inch North of magnet's end, hold in level and square. Touch the battery, then you

will see the magnet swinging East. Now put the battery
North side, positive terminal East, negative terminal
West, connect West end of the copper wire with negative
terminal, connect East end of copper wire with East side
lead, put the copper wire on top of the magnet a quarter of an inch South of magnet's end, hold the copper
wire just above in square and level, touch the positive
terminal, then you will see the magnet swinging West.
If the battery is right, magnet strong enough, and the
magnet rod balanced good it will repeat the same thing
every time.

I think the batteries are not made right. Sometimes
there is more of North Pole magnets than there is South
Pole magnets. They should be equal, the same as from
generators which do not run the South Pole magnets in
frame or base, but run directly away the same as they
run the North Pole magnets.

From the following experiment you will see that the
battery is not balanced right. Put the copper wire across
the box, one end East, the other end West, connect one
lead a foot West from East end and the other lead with
West end, hang a magnet in spider web, put the magnet
in same level with the copper wire. Keep the copper wire
end a little away from magnet's North Pole, connect East
lead with positive terminal, tap the negative terminal
several times with the loose clip, and see what the magnet is doing. Change the terminal, change the tapping,
move the box and copper wire to the South Pole end,
repeat the same thing. Then you will notice sometimes
the copper wire end pushes away the North Pole magnet,
and sometimes it pulls it in and the same thing happens
with South Pole magnet, and sometimes it does nothing.
So, it shows the battery is irregular.

Connect the leads with battery's terminals to make
a loop, keep the leads on the same level with battery,
drag a hanging magnet over the loop and the connections between the battery's terminals. You will see that
one end of the magnet keeps inside the loop, and the
other outside, and the same thing happens when the
magnet crosses the connection between the terminals.

This experiment indicates that the North and South Pole magnet currents are not only running from one terminal to the other, but are running around in an orbit and are not only running one time around, but are running many times around until the North and South Pole individual magnets get thrown out of the wire by centrifugal force, and by crowding. While the North and South Pole magnets were in their own terminals, they only possessed pushing power, the pulling power they acquire only if the other kind of magnets are in front of them, like the permanent magnets if you put the opposite magnet in front of it, then they will hold together. The same way you have done with the six inches long pieces of copper and soft iron wire.

From the experiment with the car battery, you can see the principle how permanent magnets are made by North and South Pole individual magnet currents running in a single wire from battery. How did the magnets get in there? As I said in the beginning, the North and South Pole magnets, they are the cosmic force, they hold together this earth and everything on it. Some metals and non-metals have more of the magnets than others. The North and South Pole magnets have the power to build up and take down, for instance in welding the magnets take the welding rod down and put it on the welding, in electro-plating they put one metal on the other, and if you burn a metal too much in an electric furnace the metal will disappear in air.

The North and South Pole magnets were put in the car battery by a generator. When the North and South Pole magnets went in the battery they built up a matter that held the magnets themselves, and later on the acid takes the matter in parts and separates the magnets and sends them to their own terminals, and from there they come out. In other batteries the acid takes the zinc in parts and sends the North Pole magnets to positive terminal and holds the South Pole magnets by itself for negative terminal. When the connections are made the magnets will come out of the battery and will come out until the zinc will last. When the zinc is gone the magnets are gone, too. The same is true if you put iron in acid and some other metals, for the other terminal and when the connections are made the magnets will come out of the battery, but when the iron is gone the magnets are gone, too. This should be sufficient to see that the North and South Pole magnets are holding together everything. You saw how magnetic currents are made in battery from metal by acid. Next I will tell you how magnetic currents are made by permanent and electric magnets, and then without either.

This time you will make an equipment that can be used for four purposes. Electric magnet, transformer, generator and holder of perpetual motion. Bend iron or soft steel bar one and one-half inch in diameter, bend in a U shape each prong a foot long, and three inches between the prongs, make two spools from brass or aluminum six inches long and big enough for the bar to go in. Wind fifteen hundred turns of insulated copper wire, size sixteen, on each spool. Put on as close to the bend as it will go. Connect the battery with the coils so that each current is running in both coils at the same time, and so that one end of the bar is North Pole and the other South Pole. Now you have an electric magnet.

This time the same thing will be a transformer. It will not be economical, it is only to show how a transformer works. Wind a coil of fifteen hundred turns with insulated copper wire, size eighteen, on a spool less than three inches long, so that one inch and a half square iron rod can go in easy, get two rods, one three, the other six inches long. If possible have them from laminated iron. Get two radio blue bead, six to eight-volt light bulbs. Now connect one light bulb with the three-inch coil, put the coil without a core between the loose ends of the iron prongs, connect the six-inch coils with battery, leave negative terminal open. Tap the negative terminal, then you will see the wire inside the light bulb turn red. Put iron core in the coil's hole, tap the battery, this time it will make light. Why did it not make just as much light the first time? The battery put just as much magnet in those iron prongs the first time as it did the last time, but as you see the coil did not get the magnets. Now you see the soft iron has a lot to do to make magnetic currents.

Magnetic currents, or if you want to call it electric current, make no light. We only get light if we put obstructions in the light bulbs. In the light bulbs the wire is so small that all magnets cannot pass through easily, so they heat the wire up and burn and make light. If the wire in the light bulb had been as large inside as it is outside then there would be no light. Then those individual magnets which are in the coil would dissipate in air.

Both North and South Pole individual magnet currents which came out of the car battery and went in the transformer were direct currents, but the light in the bulb was caused by alternating currents. (Have in mind that always there are two currents, one current alone cannot run. To run they have to run one against the other.) You transformed currents in kind. Now I will tell you how to transform currents in strength. To make higher voltage you wind the coil with smaller wire and more turns and to have less voltage wind the coil with bigger wire and less turns. The difference now is that this transformer makes alternating currents from direct currents and the power line transformers use alternating currents to make alternating currents in this transformer, the iron prong ends remain the same magnet pole, but in power line transformers the magnet poles alternate. In power line transformers the currents only are in motion and in this transformer the currents are in motion and you are, too.

Now about the generator. In the first place all currents are alternating. To get direct currents we have to use a commutator. Transformers and generators of any description are making the currents in the same way by filling the coil's iron core with magnets and letting the iron core push them out and into the coil. Connect the battery with the electric magnet, it will be a field magnet now. Put the three-inch coil between the iron prongs, and take it out, do it fast, repeat it, then you will have a steady light in the light bulb. Now you and the field magnet are a generator. Suppose you had a wheel and many coils around the wheel turning, then you would be making all kinds of light. Do not make the machine, I already have the application for patent in the Patent Office. I made ten different machines to make magnetic currents, but I found this combination between field magnets and coils the most efficient. Put the coil in slowly and take it out slowly, then you will have no light. That will show, to make magnetic currents, the time is important.

Put the six-inch long square rod on top of the two iron prongs, fit good so it lies even. Connect the battery with electric magnet for a little while, now disconnect the battery, connect the light bulb with the electric magnet the same way it was connected with the battery, now pull off the six-inch long bar, do it quickly, then you will see light in the bulb, connect the battery up again with the electric magnet, put the bar across the iron prongs, hold awhile, disconnect the battery. Now the electric magnet holds perpetual motion. If not disturbed it will last indefinitely. I held it in this position for six months, and when I pulled off the six-inch bar I got just as much light out of it as I got in the first time. This experiment shows that if you start the North and South Pole individual magnets in an orbit, then they will never stop. The hanging magnets that hang up and down, they show that there is motion inside the bar. Hold the perpetual motion holder North Pole magnet or pole end East and South Pole magnet terminal or pole end West, now raise it up slowly to the South Pole hanging magnet, then you will see the South Pole hanging magnet swinging South. Now put the perpetual motion holder under the North Pole hanging magnet, raise up slowly, then you will see the North Pole hanging magnet swinging North. This experiment shows without any doubt that the North and South Pole individual magnets are running in the same direction as those in the copper wire, which came out of the car battery, and in both instances while the magnets are running ahead in whirling motion they used the righthand twist.

Get that Alnico magnet, and make it so you can turn it around if possible more than two thousand revolutions a minute. Connect the light bulb with the perpetual motion holder, put it on the spinning Alnico magnet in the hole between prongs and the square iron bar, now spin the Alnico magnet around and see how much of the light you get. Now take the iron bar off, then you will get more of the light. It shows that if it is closed, some of the magnets which are in the iron prongs will run around in an orbit, and will not come out, but when the orbit is broken then they will run in the coil, and the result will be more light.

Put a paper box with plenty of iron filings in it on the horizontally spinning Alnico magnet, then you will see how the spinning magnet builds up ridges and ditches. Now put the magnet so that it can be turned vertically. Spin the magnet, then you will see the filings running against the motion and building up ridges and ditches. Put on finer filings, then there will be finer ridges and ditches. Spin one way and then the other way, then you will have some rough idea how magnets build up the matter.

You made magnetic currents in three different ways, but in principle they all were made exactly in the same way. Magnetic currents are made by concentrating, then dividing and then shifting the existing North and South Pole individual magnets from one place to another. Now I will illustrate how my best machine is doing it. I will use only one coil, and one U shape permanent magnet without using the winding that the machine uses to increase the permanent magnet strength. If you had a permanent magnet that the coil you use in the electric magnet would go in between the prongs of it, then that would be good to demonstrate, but if you have not, then use the same one you have. Get an iron core the same dimensions as in the three-inch coil, but long enough to go between the permanent magnet prongs. Wind the same number of turns and connect with the light bulb. Fasten the U shape permanent magnet very good, bend up, prongs down, North Pole North, South Pole South. Now push the coil through the prongs from West to East. Do it fast, then there will be light in the bulb, now push the coil and stop in middle, and then push again, this time you will have two lights while the coil went through the magnet prongs only once. You had two lights the first time also, but you did not notice they came in quick succession. When you pushed the coil's middle up to field magnet's middle the currents ran in one direction, and when you pushed the coil away from the field magnet's middle, then the currents reversed, then ran in the other direction. That is why you got two light flashes while the coil passed through the field magnet only one time.

Here is the way in which the North and South Pole individual magnet currents ran while you pushed the coil from West to East through the field magnet. Take the core out of the coil, wind one layer of wire on the core and make it so that the North side of the winding wire's end points East and South side of the winding wire's end points West. When you pushed the coil to the middle of the field magnet, the North Pole magnet current came out of the wire end that is pointing East, and the South Pole magnet current came out of the wire end that is pointing West, but when you pushed the coil away from the middle of the field magnet the currents reversed, then North Pole magnet current came out of the coil's wire end that is pointing West and South Pole magnet current came out of the coil's wire end that is pointing East. With the same winding if the North Pole field magnet had been southside, and South pole field magnet northside, then the running of the currents would be reversed.

When currents reverse they reverse the magnet poles in the coil. Every time when the coil is approaching the field magnets, the currents which are made in the coil during that time are making magnet poles in the coil's core ends, the same as those field magnet poles they are approaching, but during the time the coil is receding those currents are making the coil's magnet poles opposite to the field magnets they are receding from. While you have the small coil handy I will tell more about magnets. Run South Pole magnet current in the wire end that points West, and North Pole magnet current in the wire end that points East. Now North end of the coil is South Pole and South end of the coil is North Pole. Now run North Pole magnet current in West end of the wire, and South Pole magnet in East end of the wire. This time the North end of the coil will be North Pole, and South end of the coil the South Pole.

You made the one-inch-long magnets with a single wire, but if you had the same size of wire in a coil you now have and would put a bigger steel bar in the coil then you would have a bigger and stronger magnet, but to make a stronger magnet yet, you would have to wind more layers on top of the coil that you have now. When you were making the small magnets with a single copper wire you wasted too many North and South Pole individual magnets. You only got in the steel wire very small part of the magnets that came out of the copper wire. You are still wasting the North and South Pole magnets. You do not get one-half of the magnets in the steel or iron bar from those which are in the coil.

To get more magnet out of a coil put the coil in steel or iron tube, then the tube outside the coil will be a magnet the same as the coil's core, but the magnet poles will be opposite, it means at the same coil end if the core end is North Pole the tube end will be South Pole. In this way you will get almost again as much magnet out of the coil and in the core and tube. You can do better yet, join one end of the coil's core end with the same metal, joining core with tube, make two holes in end of metal for the coil wire ends to go out, fasten a ring on top, now you have the most efficient electric magnet for lifting purposes. It wastes no magnets that come from your battery or dynamo.

Take the coil out of the electric magnet, run the currents in the coil, put a hard steel bar one end to the coil's North Pole, hold awhile, take away, now the bar is a permanent magnet. That end at coil's side is South Pole magnet, and the other North Pole magnet. Now this permanent magnet can make other hard steel bars in permanent magnets but every magnet that it makes will be a weaker magnet than itself. The coil made this permanent magnet in the same way that the permanent magnets are making other permanent magnets. Put this permanent magnet in the coil's hole, reverse it, put bar's

North Pole end in coil's South Pole end, run current in the coil for a while, take the bar out, now you have a stronger permanent magnet, but the poles are reversed. This shows that the stronger magnet can change the weaker magnet.

When you were pushing the coil through the U shape magnet you got two flashes in the light bulb with one passage through the U shape magnet, and I showed you from which ends of coil's wire the currents came out while they made the flashes. Now I will make so you can actually see that it is in the way I told you. Take the light bulb off the coil, put the core in it, connect the coil with a loop that would reach six feet East from the U shape magnet. Keep the loop end a foot apart, stretch South side wire straight, make it so it cannot move. Get those little hanging magnets which hang one end up, the other down, hang the South Pole magnet on the loop wire, now push the coil through the U shape magnet and watch the hanging magnet. First it will swing South, then North. Now hang North Pole magnet on the wire, watch again while you are pushing the coil through the U shape magnet, this time first it will swing North, then South. Hang both magnets, watch again and you will see that both magnets at the same time first they swing to their own side and then to the other side. If the hanging magnets do not swing while you are pushing the coil through the U shape magnet, then the U shape magnet is not strong enough. The U shape magnet should be strong enough to lift twenty pounds. You can put two magnets together or use electric magnet, and still better you can put the coil in electric magnet, then you won't have to push it. Then you can sit down and tap the battery and see the hanging magnets swinging. All currents are made in the same way by filling the coil and iron core with North and South Pole individual magnets and then giving enough time for the magnets to get out and then start over again. If you want to use the electric magnet be sure that the North Pole is in North side, and the South Pole in South side, and put the coil in the prongs in the same way as it is now.

Now I will tell you what happened to the U shape magnet while you pushed the coil through it from West to East. Set up the three-foot magnet so it can turn, put the coil with core in it in the U shape magnet, now approach the three-foot magnet's South Pole with the U shape magnet's South Pole. As soon as the three-foot magnet begins to move you stop and mark the distance. Take the coil away, approach again as soon as the three-foot magnet begins to move away, then stop and mark the distance, then you will see how much strength the U shape magnet lost while you were pushing the coil in and halfway out of the U shape magnet. The U shape magnet was losing its strength up to the time it began to break away from the iron core, but during the time the U shape magnet broke away it regained its strength. The breaking away from the iron core recharged the U shape magnet, then it became normal again and ready for the next start. During the recharging the new supply of magnets came from the air or the earth's magnetic field.

Now we see how the magnetic currents are made by the U shape magnet. You already know that before the coil got in between the U shape magnet prongs those little individual magnets were running out of the U shape magnet prongs in all directions, but as soon as the coil's core came in effective distance from the U shape magnet's prongs then these little individual magnets began to run in the core and coil and kept running until the core broke away from the U shape magnet prongs. Now you see those little individual magnets ran out of the U shape magnet and ran in the soft iron core, but the soft iron core never held the magnets, it pushed them out. To prove it you put five or six thin iron strips on edge, slant just so they will not flop over, now approach to the ends of those strips with a magnet and you will see they flop over, hold the strips a little loose by the ends, then they will spread out. I think this is enough to show that the soft iron never held those magnets. It pushed them out. As soon as those little individual magnets get pushed out of the soft iron core then they run in the coil. When they run in the coil they are in bulk form. The coil's part is to divide those little individual magnets from bulk form in small paths. The coil is not necessary to make magnetic currents. Currents can be made with a single wire. The coil is necessary to increase the amount and strength of the currents. The coil is similar to any cell battery. One cell alone does not amount to anything. To be good, many cells have to be in a battery. The same in a coil to be good many turns have to be in a coil.

When the magnets that are in bulk form enter the coil then the coil divides them in small paths. It is done in this way. When the bulk magnets enter the coil they fill the coil's wire with North and South Pole individual magnets. North Pole magnets pointing toward South Pole U shape magnet and South Pole pointing toward North Pole U shape magnet. Now the wire in the coil is one continuous magnet. One side of the wire is South Pole and the other North Pole. Now we have those little North and South Pole individual magnets in the wire, but they are not running in the way we want. They are running across the wire. We want the magnets to run through the wire lengthwise, but there is only one way to do it, we have to increase the number of those North and South Pole individual magnets. To do it the coil will have to approach and enter the U shape magnet, but when the coil reaches the middle of the U shape magnet the limit is there so the running of the currents stop. In the core and the coil there is plenty of those little magnets, but they stopped to run through the wire lengthwise, now they run only across the coil's wire, to make the magnets run in the wire lengthwise again the coil will have to get away from the U shape magnet. As soon as the coil begins to move away from the U shape magnet, then those little North and South Pole individual magnets begin to run again through the wire lengthwise, but in opposite direction until the magnets in the iron core are gone.

I told you that the coil is a magnet during the time the currents are made, now I will show you. Get a small paper box to go in between the prongs of the U shape magnet, put iron filings in it. Wrap six-inch long soft iron wire with paper, put the wire in box in iron filings, now put the box between the U shape magnet prongs. Raise the wire up, then you will see filing strands clinging to the insulated iron wire. Raise the wire up slowly, then the filing strands will sag and fall, take the box out, put the wire in the filings again, raise up and you will see that the wire is no magnet, but during the time it was between the U shape magnet prongs it was a magnet. This shows that during the time the coil moves through the U shape magnet the coil becomes a magnet, but its function is double. Some individual North and South Pole magnets run through the coil's wire crosswise, and some run through the coil's wire lengthwise.

Maybe you think that it is not fair to use iron wire to demonstrate how magnetic currents are made, but I can tell you that if I do not use iron core in the coil I can make more of the magnetic currents with soft iron wire coil than I can with copper wire coil, so you see it is perfectly good to use iron wire to demonstrate how magnetic currents are made. You can do the same thing with the copper wire in using iron filings, but only on a smaller scale.

You saw how the magnets are running through a wire crosswise. Now I will tell you how they are running through the wire lengthwise. Before the magnets start to run through the wire lengthwise they are lined up in a square across the wire, one side of the wire is North Pole magnet side and the other side is South Pole magnet side. When the coil begins to approach the middle of the U shape magnet and the currents begin to run then the magnets which are in the wire begin to slant, North Pole magnets pointing East the same as the coil's wire end, where the North Pole magnet current came out and South Pole magnets pointing West the same as the coil's wire end where the South Pole magnet current came out. When the coil reaches the middle of the U shape magnet then the currents stop to run. Now the North and South Pole magnets are pointing across the wire again. When the coil begins to move away from the middle of the U shape magnet and the currents begin to run then the magnets which are in the wire begin to slant, but this time the North Pole magnets are pointing West the same as the coil's wire end where the North Pole magnet current came out and South Pole magnets pointing East the same as the coil's wire end where the South Pole magnet current came out. When the coil moves out of the U shape magnet's effective distance the currents running stop. This is the way the alternating currents are made.

When the individual North and South pole magnets are running through a wire lengthwise they are running in slant and whirling around while running ahead. You can see the slant by watching the sparks when you are putting together and pulling away soft iron wire ends which are connected to the battery by their other ends. To see how the currents are running out of the coil's wire watch those six one-inch-long magnets which lie on the glass. Put those magnets together with ends even, then let them loose, then you will see that they will roll away and if the magnets be stronger then they will roll away farther. This is the way the North and South Pole individual magnets are running out of the coil's wire lengthwise. The reason the North and South Pole individual magnets do not run across through the coil's wire as fast out as they run in while the coil is between the U shape magnet, the coil's wire is insulated, there is an air space around every wire and as it is known that the dry air is the best obstruction for the magnets to go through and as you know the coil is well insulated so the damp air does not get in. It is well known that it is many times easier for the magnets to run in metal than in air, now you see when the magnets run in the wire they hesitate to run out of the wire across the same way as they came in, so more of the new magnets are coming in the wire crosswise, than they can get out crosswise, so they get pushed out through the wire lengthwise. Now you know how the alternating magnetic currents are made.

You have been wondering why alternating currents can run so far away from their generators. One reason is between every time the currents start and stop there is no pressure in the wire so the magnets from the air run in the wire and when the run starts there already are magnets in the wire which do not have to come from the generator, so the power line itself is a small generator which assists the big generator to furnish the magnets for the currents to run with. I have a generator that generates currents on a small scale from the air without using any magnets around it.

Another thing, you have been wondering how a U shape permanent magnet can keep its normal strength indefinitely. You know the soft iron does not hold magnets, but you already have one that holds it. It is the perpetual motion holder. It illustrates the principle how permanent magnets are made. All that has to be done is to start the magnets to run in an orbit, then they will never stop. Hard steel U shape magnets have a broken orbit, but under proper conditions it is permanent. I think the structure of the metal is the answer. I have two U shape magnets. They look alike, but one is a little harder than the other. The harder one can lift three pounds more than the softer one. I have been tempering the other steel magnets, and have noticed that the harder the steel gets the smaller it becomes. That shows that the metal is more packed and has less holes in it so the magnets cannot pass through it in full speed, so they dam up in the prong ends. They come in faster than they can get out. I think the ability for the soft steel welding rod to hold magnets is in the metal's fine structure.

The reason I call the results of North and South Pole magnet's functions magnetic currents and not electric currents or electricity is the electricity is connected too much with those non-existing electrons. If it had been called magneticity then I would accept it. Magneticity would indicate that it has a magnetic base and so it would be all right.

As I said in the beginning, the North and South Pole magnets they are the cosmic force. They hold together this earth and everything on it, and they hold together the moon, too. The moon's North end holds South Pole magnets the same as the earth's North end. The moon's South end holds North Pole magnets the same as the earth's South end. Those people who have been wondering why the moon does not come down all they have to do is to give the moon one-half of a turn so that the North end would be in South side, and South end in the North side, and then the moon would come down. At present the earth and the moon have like magnet poles in the same sides so their own magnet poles keep themselves apart, but when the poles are reversed, then they will pull together. Here is a good tip to the rocket people. Make the rocket's head strong North Pole magnet, and the tail end strong South Pole magnet, and then shut to on the moon's North end, then you will have better success.

North and South Pole magnets are not only holding together the earth and moon, but they are turning the earth around on its axis. Those magnets which are coming down from the sun they are hitting their own kind of magnets which are circulating around the earth and they hit more on the East side than on the West side, and that is what makes the earth turn around. North and South Pole magnets make the lightning, in earth's North hemisphere the South Pole magnets are going up and the North pole magnets are coming down in the same flash. In the earth's South hemisphere the North Pole magnets are going up and the South Pole magnets are coming down in the same flash. The North lights are caused by the North and South Pole magnets passing in concentrated streams, but the streams are not as much concentrated as they are in the lightning. The radio waves are made by the North and South Pole magnets. Now about the magnet size. You know sunlight can go through glass, paper and leaves, but it cannot go through wood, rock and iron, but the magnets can go through everything. This shows that each magnet is smaller than each particle of light.